KOOKY SPOOKS

How many differences can you find between these two pictures?

GOAT TELL YOUR MOTHER

There are plenty of fruits and vegetables to be picked in this farmyard. Use the clues to gather the letters that will give you the answer to the first goat's question. The clue numbers tell you where to put the right letters in the spaces. The first letter has already been picked to get you started.

1 - The first letter is on the tree that George Washington is believed to have chopped down.

2 - Now pick the letter from the vines that some say belong to a vegetable and some say belong to a fruit.

3 - This letter is attached to a long vegetable that rabbits like.

4 - This letter is on the fruit tree that sounds like there are two things together.

5 - After you pick the letter from this red fruit tree, you shouldn't have to go to the doctor today.

6 - Stalk the vegetables that are all ears and you'll find letter number six.

7 - Halloween is the best time to get the letter from these big vegetables.

8 - The eighth letter is in the vineyard, attached to fruits that are good for jelly, jam and juice.

9 - There is a fruit that shares its name with its color. That's where you can get the next letter.

10 - The yellow covering on this fruit can't be eaten, but they make good slippers.

11 - The next letter is hiding among the leaves near the heads of these leafy green vegetables.

12 - This vegetable only has eyes for you.

Illustrated by Lynn Adams

WHERE THE WOOLIES LIVE

The Woolies are a tribe of hat hunters. They will stalk any jungle or swim any ocean just to get the newest in headgear. From the clues, can you figure out which island is home to the wild Woolies?

Illustrated by Terry Rogers

The Woolies' island does not have a volcano.
There is a stream on the Woolies' island.
There is no snow on their island.
The Woolies' island is not between any other islands.

Answer on page 47.

THE TIME MACHINE

Becky built a time machine and threw it into reverse. She's gone back in time, but to where? Will she see knights or cave people? Use your imagination to draw the scene outside her window to let Becky know when and where she landed.

RED ALERT

Illustrated by Jon Davis

TIME

HOME

FORWARD

REVERSE

BRAKE

START

7

WINDOW WATCH

Can you find which two sections of this window are exactly alike?

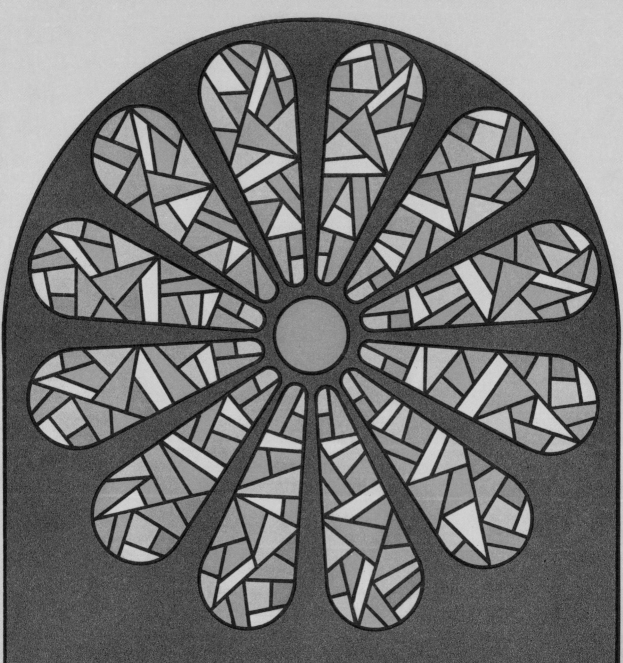

Answer on page 47.

AWFULLY ODD

Can you follow the path, using only odd numbers to get from IN to OUT? You can move across, backward, up, or down. You cannot move diagonally.

IN

23	34	7	21	3	99	49	61	33	20	51	39	55	21
19	86	68	2	95	56	37	44	91	66	17	82	9	88
15	55	37	93	79	28	90	2	13	12	43	28	91	37
14	32	70	50	46	23	5	72	45	21	65	36	50	23
16	47	66	13	7	15	10	1	54	30	72	44	9	87
25	33	54	1	81	21	5	19	7	51	88	10	17	6
47	94	12	80	9	58	94	36	48	39	16	3	89	21
29	8	13	35	79	22	51	95	24	11	51	69	81	38
52	11	67	92	42	82	13	28	57	78	64	30	4	26
39	1	26	8	41	71	25	64	31	18	44	96	12	74
50	41	84	30	59	5	49	21	19	45	14	27	48	2
62	29	33	76	14	23	67	33	77	82	7	39	61	15
9	22	57	40	32	82	98	2	23	60	91	88	41	90
17	16	73	35	85	89	21	39	13	85	95	6	87	39

OUT

Illustrated by Barbara Gray

Answer on page 47.

ANIMAL CELEBRITIES

The animal kingdom has sent out its biggest celebrities to meet the public. Each of these animals is a character in a book or story. Your job is to identify the kind of animal represented by each character. For example, for Winnie-the-Pooh the answer would be BEAR. Fill in as many animals as you can. Look for letter clues to help uncover some of the animals you aren't familiar with. We've done two to get you started.

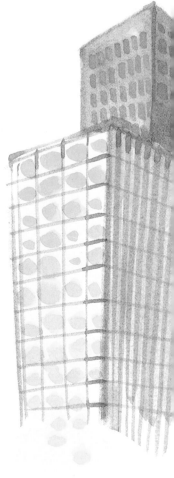

ACROSS

2. Wol
5. Rikki-Tikki-Tavi
7. Rascal
9. Dab-Dab
10. Henny Penny
13. ~~Veronica~~
15. Pretzel
18. Monstro
19. ~~Kermit~~
21. Buford
23. Yertle
24. Flopsy
26. Paddington
27. Walter
28. Thidwick

DOWN

1. Roo
3. Aslan
4. Stuart
5. George
6. Babar
8. Bagheera
9. Eeyore
11. Wilbur
12. Charlotte
13. Black Beauty
14. Kaa
16. Bambi
17. Templeton
19. Puss-in-Boots
20. Ferdinand
22. Polynesia
25. Shere Khan

The story for each character is listed on page 50.

Answer on page 47.

WHERE TO LOOK

Paula is having a busy day. Luckily, there are lots of things that will help her keep track of what she needs to know. Take one of her choices and put it on the line where it will provide the best answer to Paula's questions. The first one has been done for you.

Answer on page 47.

Thermometer   Dictionary
Cookbook   Address book
Speedometer   Telephone book
Almanac   Clock
Newspaper   TV schedule
  Atlas
  ~~Gas gauge~~

1. Does mom's car need gas?

   Gas gauge

2. What ingredients do I need to bake muffins?

   _____

3. What time is it now?

   _____

4. What's Uncle Mel's zip code?

   _____

5. How hot is it today?

   _____

6. What's the phone number for take-out pizza?

   _____

7. Who won yesterday's ball game?

   _____

8. How fast can mom's car go?

   _____

9. Where is Bora Bora?

   _____

10. What's on television tomorrow night?

    _____

11. How much rain did we have last year?

    _____

12. What does "arroyo" mean?

    _____

Illustrated by R. Michael Palan

FREE FOR ALL

How fortunate you are to have this puzzle. For one thing, each of the words below begins with the word FOR. Use the clues to help form your thoughts about what each word is.

1. for ___   An eating utensil

2. for ___ ___   Strength or power

3. for ___ ___   A place where metal is hammered and molded

4. for ___ ___ ___   To put out of one's memory

5. for ___ ___ ___   Dressed in the correct manner, opposite of casual

6. for ___ ___ ___   A large area of land covered by trees

7. for ___ ___ ___ ___   Opposite of backward

8. for ___ ___ ___ ___   At all times; through endless ages

9. for ___ ___ ___ ___   To give up without a struggle

10. for ___ ___ ___ ___   Not native to the country in which it is found

11. for ___ ___ ___ ___   Luck or chance affecting the events of one's life

12. for ___ ___ ___ ___ ___   A tennis stroke

13. for ___ ___ ___ ___ ___   To predict the weather

14. for ___ ___ ___ ___ ___   In olden times, a measurement of two weeks

Answer on page 47.

Illustrated by Richard Johnson

EYE FOOLERS

Each of these questions asks something about the picture next to it. Give your best answer, but be careful. These things are definitely not what they seem.

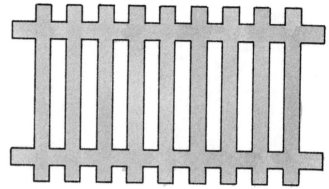

1. Is this a picture fence or railroad tracks?

2. Is this letter "E" toppling forward or sinking down?

3. Is this bird flying to the left or to the right?

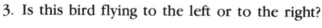

4. Does your eye see a river or a tree?

Illustrated by Rob Sepanak

5. Can you find the girl in the flower?

6. Are these pointed arches

continuous or broken?

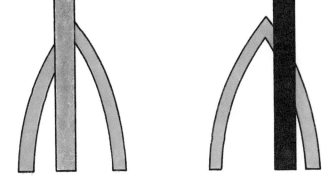

7. What is the matter with this circle?

8. Is the church tower longer than

the base of the church?

SENTENCE SHOPPING

There are a variety of foods and drink hiding in these sentences. For example, look at this sentence:

Hurry, so dad won't be late.

Did you find "soda" hiding between so and dad? A good shopper will be able to pick out all ten of the other hidden items. The letters will always appear in order and won't be jumbled.

Answer on page 48.

1. He had a pet hamster in the cage.

2. She'll fish all day off that pier.

3. The car rots in the junk yard.

4. Is Rob ready to go to the game?

5. The bee flew onto the flower.

6. It was a real amber-colored monster.

7. We could pet each animal at this special zoo.

8. The magician could spin a chair.

9. Let the best ring be answered.

10. We found the spot at Oester Street and River Lane.

Illustrated by John Nez

INSTANT PICTURE

Does this picture ring a bell? It might once you fill in every space containing two dots.

Illustrated by Rob Sepanak

Answer on page 48.

SNOW CODE

Using the snowflake alphabet below, see if you can figure out this funny poem by Michael Flanders.

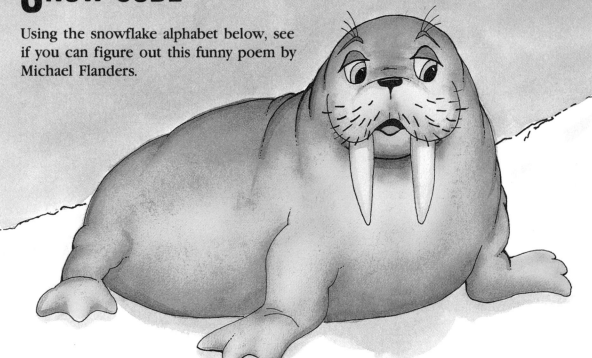

 =A   =H   =O   =U

=B   =I   =P   =V

=C   =J   =Q   =W

=D   =K   =R   =X

=E   =L   =S   =Y

=F   =M   =T   =Z

=G   =N

    Illustrated by Rob Sepanak

_____ ___ _____ _____

___ ___ _____ _____ _____

_____ _____

____ _____ .

___ ___ _____ _____

_____ _____

____ _____ ___ _____

LACE TRACE

Dora can't make heads or tails of her feet. Her shoes are a tangled mess. See if you can follow her laces to find which shoes are attached to which knots.

Answer on page 48.

STOP, LOOK, AND LIST

Under each category list one thing that begins with every letter. For example, one City Place that begins with "B" is a Building. See if you can name another.

CITY PLACES

B _____

L _____

S _____

P _____

R _____

NURSERY RHYME/ FAIRY TALE FOLKS

B _____

L _____

S _____

P _____

R _____

THINGS WORN BESIDES CLOTHING

B _____

L _____

S _____

P _____

R _____

Illustrated by Lisa Dayer

Answer on page 48.

HIDDEN PICTURES

How many objects can you find hidden in this picture?

Illustrated by Lynn Adams

ROW, ROW, ROW

Each flag has something in common with the two others in the same row. For example, in the top row across, each flag has an animal on it. Look at the other rows across, down, and diagonally. What's the same about each row of three?

Mexico

Fiji

Bolivia

St. Helena

Belize

Ecuador

Dominica

Nauru

Paraguay

Answer on page 48.

WHAT'S IN A WORD?

Lots of good food can be found in a CAFETERIA, but at least forty smaller words can be found hiding there, too. CAFE and TEAR are just two of the words you may find. How many other words of three letters or more can you make out of the letters in CAFETERIA?

Answer on page 48.

PICTURE MIXER

Copy these mixed-up squares in the spaces on the next page to put this picture back together. The letters and numbers tell you where each square belongs. The first one, **A-3**, has been done for you.

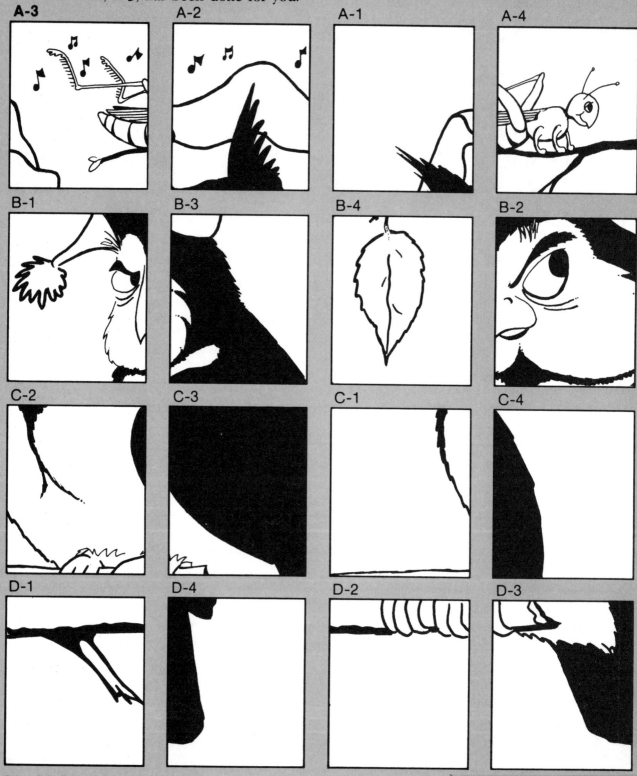

Illustrated by Rob Sepanak

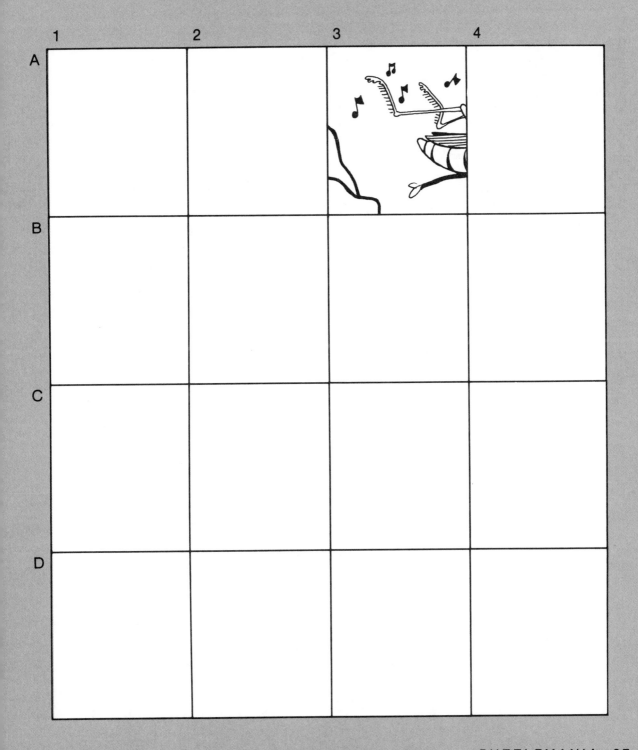

CLASS ACT

The job titles of people who work in schools are scrambled on this page. See if you can unscramble them before the bell rings and class begins.

CHACO

TRACERYES

ERUNS

ARETCHE

TUBESTITSU HEARTEC

TORNIMO

PAPIRLINC

OCKO

CANDIEGU SNORECOLU

TORANIJ

CHARTEE'S IDEA

BRAINRAIL

Answer on page 49.

Illustrated by R. Michael Palan

WHAT AM I?

I am a small, carnivorous (meat-eating) animal that can be found throughout the United States.

I am a relative of the genus PROCYON, and of the family PROCYONIDAE.

This makes me a relative of the bear family.

I hunt for poultry, mice, fish, frogs, insects, and bird's eggs. For variety, I sometimes also eat nuts and wild fruit.

I hibernate during the winter, which means I sleep from autumn until spring.

I am a nocturnal animal, and mainly come out at night.

I am a very good swimmer.

If water is available, I always wash my food before eating it.

I have rings on my tail and a black "mask" on my face.

What Am I?

Answer on page 49.

Illustrated by Barbara Gray

CHECK AGAIN

How many things can you find wrong in this picture?

0:32 MIN.

Illustrated by Anni Matsick

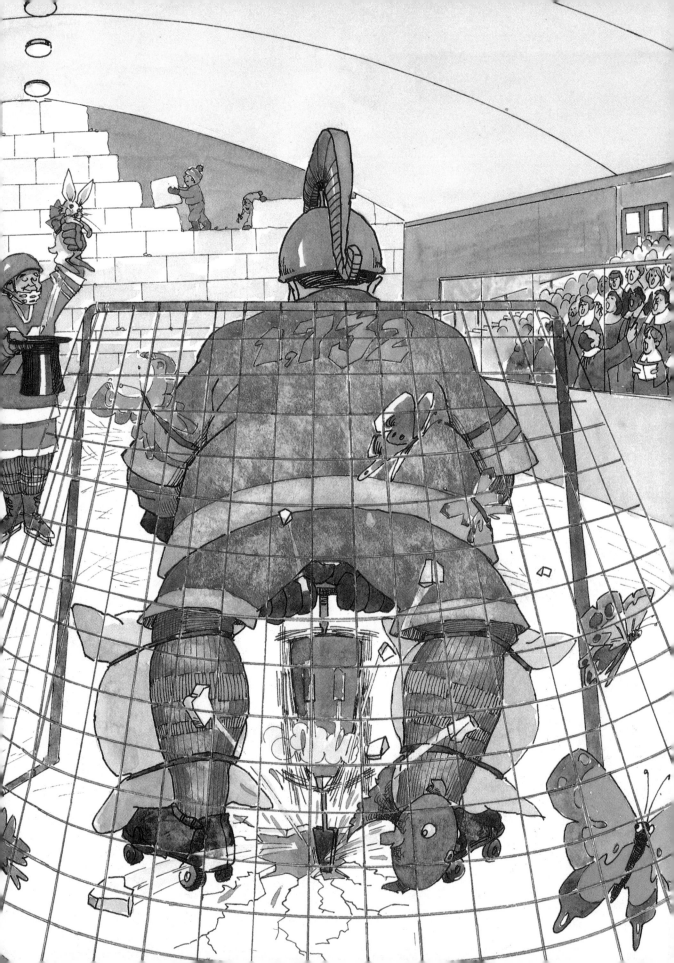

SPOON SPOOF

There are at least 30 spoons hidden in this picture.
How many can you find?

Illustrated by John Nez

OFF TO BED

Some items that might be found in your bedroom are listed below. See if you can tuck them all into the right spaces. Use the size of each word as a clue to where it belongs. Each word is used only once, so cross it off the list when you've found the spot for it to rest.

3 LETTERS
Bed

4 LETTERS
Bunk   Lamp
Desk   Toys

5 LETTERS
Alarm   Radio
Books   Sleep
Dream

6 LETTERS
Closet   Pillow
Covers   Sheets

7 LETTERS
Blanket   Posters
Clothes   Privacy
Dresser   Shelves

8 LETTERS
Mattress

Illustrated by Barbara Gray

Answer on page 49.

JACK AND THE BEANSTALK

Oh no! Jack was almost away from the castle, but the harp sang out. Now Jack is running from the giant. Help Jack find a way through the clouds and down the beanstalk to get home safely.

Answer on page 49.

Illustrated by John Nez

UP, UP, AND AWAY

Bobbi and her family wanted to tour the valley. They came up with an unusual way to do it. Can you put their pictures in order to show what they did first, second, and so on?

Illustrated by Judith Hunt

Answer on page 49.

RECYCLING MEMORIES

Take a long look at this picture. Try to remember everything you see in it. Then turn the page, and try to answer some questions about it without looking back.

Illustrated by Anni Matsick

DON'T READ THIS UNTIL YOU HAVE LOOKED AT "Recycling Memories—Part 1" ON PAGE 37.

RECYCLING MEMORIES   Part 2

Can you answer these questions about the scene you saw? Don't peek!

1. What went in the last bin to the right?
2. What did the boy have in his wagon?
3. How much were they paying for aluminum?
4. What color streamers were on the girl's bicycle?
5. Who was running this recycling campaign?
6. What was the older man doing?
7. How much paper was on the scale?
8. What day of the week was it?
9. How many animals were in the scene?
10. What were all the scouts wearing?

Answer on page 49.

HANG-UPS

Can you find something wrong with any of these coat hangers?

Illustrated by Rob Sepanak

Answer on page 49.

DOT MAGIC

This little duck is all quacked up if he thinks he's talking to his mother. Follow the numbers to connect the dots and show the little guy who he's really talking to.

Answer on page 49.

NATIVE AMERICANS

Just as Native Americans once spread across the entire country, the names of 55 Native American nations and tribes are spread throughout the letters on the next page. Look across, backward, up, down, and diagonally to find them all.

Acoma	Haida	Missouri	Ottawa	Sioux
Algonquin	Hare	Modoc	Paiute	Susquehanna
Apache	Hopi	Mohawk	Pima	Taos
Arapaho	Hupa	Mohegan	Pueblo	Ute
Cherokee	Illinois	Narraganset	Quapaw	Yaqui
Cree	Iowa	Navajo	Sac	Zia
Crow	Iroquois	Nez Perce	Santee	Zuni
Delaware	Kiowa	Oglala	Sarsi	
Dogrib	Kutchin	Ojibwa	Seminole	
Erie	Massachusetts	Omaha	Seneca	
Eskimo	Miami	Onondaga	Shawnee	
Fox	Micmac	Oto	Shoshoni	

Illustrated by R. Michael Palan

```
A N A G E H O M A W O I K I
R A C O M A G A D N O N O R
A R I V L C A M C I M L I U
P R L A I U Q A Y Z B M X O
A A L B I R G O D E A A U S
H G I N O Z M I U I T P O S
O A N T U A K P M F A U I I
T N O N H I N O H S O H S M
T S I A P A C H E E S X H A
A E S N A V A J O S R T A S
W T S N P I M A J K M I R S
A K I A A M I L I I C R E A
P U O H I O O O B M H E C C
A T U E U D A H W O E E R H
U C Q U T O Z C A A R N E U
Q H O Q E C R E E W O W P S
C I R S A R S I Q N K A Z E
R N I U Q N O G L A E H E T
O C A S E M I N O L E S N T
W D E L A W A R E E T N A S
```

Answer on page 49.

PAPER PROBLEM

Joey has a paper route. His first stop every morning is Elaine Drive. From the clues below, can you figure out in what order Joey delivers his papers, and who lives in each house?

CLUES:

1. The Smiths, who live in the green house, get their paper after the people in the blue house but before the people on the other corner.

2. Mr. Black, whose house color starts with the same letter and has the same number of letters as his last name, has to wait until right after Mr. Brown gets his paper.

3. The red house, which is the Jones's house, is always last.

4. Mr. Brown, who lives alone in a house of a color different than his name, likes his paper first thing in the morning.

5. The other families are the Golds and the Whites. Neither family lives in a house with the same color as its name.

Illustrated by Jon Davis

Answer on page 50.

SOMETHING TO NEVER FORGET

If you follow the directions, and cross off the right words in columns A, B, and C, you will find out an interesting fact.

1. Cross off the names of colors in columns A and C.
2. Cross off the names of farm animals in the even-numbered rows.
3. Cross off the names of clothing in the even-numbered rows.
4. Cross off the names of red and green vegetables in the odd-numbered rows.
5. Cross off the names of foods that can be orange in column A.
6. Cross off the names of furniture you would find in a house.
7. Cross off the names of things with wheels in columns B and C.
8. Cross off the names of shapes in the odd-numbered rows.
9. Cross off the names of things found in the sky in columns A, B, and C.
10. Cross off the names of things that fly in the even-numbered rows.

	A	B	C
1.	BEET	BUS	AN
2.	SUN	COW	SHOES
3.	ELEPHANT	SQUARE	ORANGE
4.	RED	CHAIR	BICYCLE
5.	CARROT	IS	BEAN
6.	PIG	HAT	THE
7.	BLUE	ONLY	PINK
8.	SOCKS	CAR	HORSE
9.	ANIMAL	TABLE	GREEN
10.	CHEESE	MOON	THAT
11.	YELLOW	HAS	TRUCK
12.	BIRDS	SHEEP	STARS
13.	CIRCLE	FOUR	PEAS
14.	CHICKEN	CAP	AIRPLANE
15.	KNEES	BED	PURPLE

Answer on page 50.

43

RHYME CLIMB

Professor Hink Pink is out and about again. On this trip, he went rhyming climbing. He climbed a hill with skill, gathering things that rhyme. One thing he has is his bent tent. See how many other rhymes you can find.

TOOT! TOOT!

Illustrated by Terry Rogers

Answer on page 50.

OOPS!

Read the following paragraphs carefully. Each contains an error for you to find. The answer to the first one is given to help you get started.

1. When we traveled to Canada, it was fun seeing Niagara Falls, orange groves and a copper mine. (Oops, no orange groves that far north!)

2. Today is the birthday of the twin brothers, John Smith and Mary Johnson.

3. Martins' Grocery has a sale on berries— blackberries, strawberries, black cherries, and raspberries.

4. "I love any music made by strings," Cheryl said. "Piano, harp, violin, guitar, and xylophone."

5. A restaurant advertised a lunch composed of foods that could be eaten with the fingers. They offered soup and crackers, tuna sandwiches, carrot and celery sticks, and raisin cookies.

6. "I remember exactly when I broke my leg," Fred said. "It was Feb. 30, 1988."

7. Wright's Shoe Shoppe has a clearance sale on footwear. They're offering 50% off on shoes, socks, slippers, gloves, and boots.

8. "We've visited five state capitals," Sue said, "Lansing, Michigan; Chicago, Illinois; Indianapolis, Indiana; Madison, Wisconsin; and Des Moines, Iowa."

Answer on page 50.

Wright's Shoe Shoppe

Wright's

50% OFF SALE

M. Nadel

ANSWERS

GOAT TELL YOUR MOTHER (pages 4-5)
He's my kid brother.

WHERE THE WOOLIES LIVE (page 6)

WINDOW WATCH (page 8)

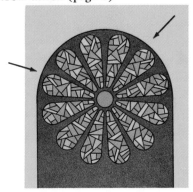

AWFULLY ODD (page 9)

ANIMAL CELEBRITIES (pages 10-11)

WHERE TO LOOK (page 12)

1. Gas gauge	7. Newspaper
2. Cookbook	8. Speedometer
3. Clock	9. Atlas
4. Address book	10. TV schedule
5. Thermometer	11. Almanac
6. Telephone book	12. Dictionary

FREE FOR ALL (page 13)
1. fork
2. force
3. forge
4. forget
5. formal
6. forest
7. forward
8. forever
9. forfeit
10. foreign
11. fortune
12. forehand
13. forecast
14. fortnight

EYE FOOLERS (pages 14-15)
1-4. Your eye will give you different answers for some of these questions.
5. The girl's face is in one of the petals of the flower.
6. The arches are continuous. It's the bars that make them appear broken.
7. There's nothing wrong with the circle. The lines make it appear flat.
8. The base and the tower are the same length.

SENTENCE SHOPPING (page 16)

1. ham (in the word: hamster)
2. shellfish (in the words: she'll fish)
3. carrots (in the words: car & rots)
4. bread (in the words: Rob & ready)
5. beef (in the words: bee & flew)
6. lamb (in the words: real & amber)
7. tea (in the words: pet & each)
8. spinach (in the words: spin, a, & chair)
9. string beans (in the words: best, ring, be, & answered)
10. potatoes (in the words: spot, at & Oester)

INSTANT PICTURE (page 17)

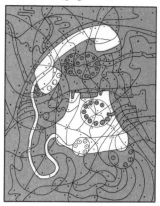

SNOW CODE (pages 18-19)

THE WALRUS LIVES
ON ICY FLOES
AND UNSUSPECTING
ESKIMOES.
DON'T BRING YOUR
WIFE TO ARCTIC TUNDRA
A WALRUS MAY BOB
UP FROM UNDRA.

LACE TRACE (page 20)

STOP, LOOK, AND LIST (page 21)

Here are our answers. You may have found others.

City Places	Nursery Rhyme/Fairy Tale Folks
Bus Stop	Big Bad Wolf
Library	Little Boy Blue
Skyscraper	Simple Simon
Park	Peter Piper
Restaurant	Red Riding Hood

Things Worn Besides Clothing
Belt
Locket
Scarf
Pin
Ring

ROW, ROW, ROW (page 24)

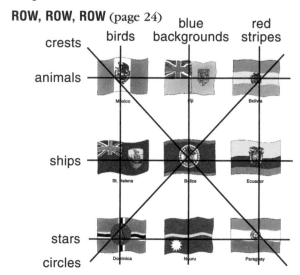

WHAT'S IN A WORD? (page 25)

Here are the answers we found. You may have found some others.

ace	fate
act	fear
air	feat
arc	fee
are	feet
area	fierce
art	fire
ate	fit
cafe	free
car	ice
care	irate
cart	race
cat	raft
cater	rat
craft	rate
crate	react
create	reef
ear	rice
eat	tar
era	tea
face	tear
fact	tee
fair	tie
far	tire
farce	trace
fare	tree
fat	

PICTURE MIXER (pages 26-27)

CLASS ACT (page 28)

Coach	Substitute Teacher	Guidance Counselor
Secretary	Monitor	Janitor
Nurse	Principal	Teacher's Aide
Teacher	Cook	Librarian

WHAT AM I? (page 29)
A raccoon

OFF TO BED (page 33)

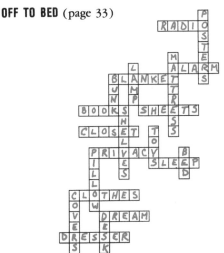

JACK AND THE BEANSTALK (pages 34-35)

UP, UP, AND AWAY (page 36)

1	3
5	2
6	4

RECYCLING MEMORIES (page 38)
1. Glass
2. Newspapers and a cat.
3. Aluminum was 25 cents a pound.
4. The streamers were yellow.
5. Boy Scout Troop 184.
6. He was picking up a can.
7. There were 15 pounds of paper on the scale.
8. Saturday
9. There were two dogs, a cat, a butterfly, and a bird.
10. They wore T-shirts with the scout symbol.

HANG-UPS (page 38)

DOT MAGIC (page 39)

NATIVE AMERICANS (pages 40-41)

PAPER PROBLEM (page 42)

The Smiths live in the green house. They are not first or last.

The Joneses live in the red house and are last, or sixth, as stated in clue 3.

Mr. Brown gets his paper first, in clue 4, and then Mr. Black gets his paper next, clue 2. Mr. Black can only live in the brown house because of the points in clue 2.

The Smiths must get their paper in fourth position, because they are right after the blue house, which can't belong to Black or Brown. The Smiths must also be before the white house, which must be fifth, because the red house is last.

Since the Whites can't live in the white house, clue 5, they must live in the blue one. So they get their paper third. This leaves the Golds to live in the white house.

So the answer is:

House color	Family Name	Receives Paper Number
Yellow	Brown	1
Brown	Black	2
Blue	White	3
Green	Smith	4
White	Gold	5
Red	Jones	6

SOMETHING TO NEVER FORGET (page 43)

AN ELEPHANT IS THE ONLY ANIMAL THAT HAS FOUR KNEES.

The words to be crossed off under each set of instructions are:
1. RED, BLUE, YELLOW, ORANGE, PINK, GREEN, PURPLE
2. COW, PIG, SHEEP, CHICKEN
3. SHOES, HAT, SOCKS, CAP
4. BEET, BEAN, PEAS
5. CARROT, CHEESE
6. CHAIR, TABLE, BED
7. BUS, CAR, BICYCLE, TRUCK
8. SQUARE, CIRCLE
9. SUN, MOON, STARS
10. BIRDS, AIRPLANE

RHYME CLIMB (pages 44-45)

Among the things the Professor found were a:
bee tree
wing sling
map cap
snake cake
hot pot
stick brick
frog log
sun bun
path bath
owl towel
toot boots
black backpack
stag flag
regal eagle
mountain fountain
maroon balloon
fox box
bear chair
hawk fork
colder boulder

OOPS! (page 46)

1. There are no orange groves that far north.
2. Twins should have the same last name, and Mary is a sister.
3. Black cherries aren't berries.
4. A xylophone has no strings.
5. Soup isn't a finger food.
6. February never has 30 days.
7. Gloves aren't footwear.
8. Springfield is the capital of Illinois, not Chicago.

ANIMAL CELEBRITIES (pages 10-11)

Eeyore, Roo, Wol—*Winnie-the-Pooh* by A.A. Milne
Charlotte, Templeton, Wilbur—*Charlotte's Web* by E.B. White
Dab-Dab, Polynesia—*The Story of Dr. Dolittle* by Hugh Lofting
Bagheera, Kaa, Shere Khan—*The Jungle Book* by Rudyard Kipling
Yertle—*Yertle the Turtle* by Dr. Seuss
Thidwick—*Thidwick, the Big Hearted Moose* by Dr. Seuss
Ferdinand—*The Story of Ferdinand* by Munro Leaf
Paddington—*Paddington Series* by Michael Bond
Stuart—*Stuart Little* by E.B. White
Pretzel—*Pretzel* by H.A. Rey
Kermit—*Kermit the Hermit* by Bill Peet

George—*Curious George Series* by H. A. Rey
Buford—*Buford the Little Bighorn* by Bill Peet
Veronica—*Veronica and the Birthday Present* by Roger Duvoisin
Bambi—*Bambi* by Felix Salten
Aslan—*The Lion, the Witch and the Wardrobe* by C.S. Lewis
Rascal—*Rascal* by Sterling North
Flopsy—*Tales of Peter Rabbit* by Beatrix Potter
Puss-In-Boots—*Stories of Times Past* by Charles Perrault
Monstro—*Pinocchio* by Carlo Lorenzini
Babar—*The Babar Series* by L. de Brunhoff
Henny Penny—*English Fairy Tale* by Joseph Jacobs
Walter—*Walter the Wolf* by Marjorie Shermat
Black Beauty—*Black Beauty* by Anna Sewell